The Grea
Canal Clean Up

by Antony Wootten
Illustrated by Amit Tayal

OXFORD

UNIVERSITY PRESS

Chapter 1
Duck in distress

Jack trudged through the city's <u>central</u> park, his school bag hanging from his shoulders. He headed down the steps to the canal with its rows of colourful boats. A lonely crisp packet tumbled along the path in front of him. In the distance, he could see the afternoon sun glinting on the windows of the boat where he and his mum lived.

Where in the city do you think the <u>central</u> park would be?

Jack stamped on the crisp packet and then bent down to pick it up. The sight of all the litter in the hedges made him sigh. He wished there were more rubbish bins along the canal path.

Jack heard footsteps behind him. Glancing over his shoulder, he saw Nadia, a new girl in his class. He thought about waiting for her but decided not to.

"I don't really know her," he thought.

Up ahead, a green-headed duck was quacking loudly. It had two black curled tail feathers. Jack had often seen it waddling about on the path or swimming near the boats.

As Jack got closer, he realized that the duck was in distress. Jack dropped his school bag and walked slowly towards the duck. One of its legs was tangled in a plastic bag.

Carefully, Jack freed the duck's leg. It was eager to get back in the water and flapped its wings. Startled, Jack stepped back, slipped on some wet mud, and fell backwards.

Jack got to his feet. His trousers were smeared with mud. To make matters worse, Nadia was standing there, grinning.

Jack didn't know what to say.

Luckily, Nadia spoke first. "Good job you came along when you did," she said. She nodded at the duck, which was now calmly bobbing in the water nearby and quacking loudly. "I think it's saying thanks," she added.

Some loud voices made Jack and Nadia look around. Further along the path, there was a group of teenagers, using a tin can as a football. As they passed Jack and Nadia, a tall boy threw his empty water bottle down. It bounced off the path into the canal, landing near the duck Jack had rescued. The duck flapped its wings and paddled further away.

Angrily, Jack opened his mouth to object, but the words stuck in his throat.

"Hey!" Nadia said, scowling at the boy. "Don't do that!"

Ignoring her, the tall boy kicked the can towards his friend. Nadia sprang forward. Her foot made <u>contact</u> with the can. She flicked it with her toe. It flew into the air then dropped into a nearby bin.

Everyone stared at Nadia, amazed.

"Wow!" Jack gasped.

Nadia's foot made <u>contact</u> with the tin can.
Does this mean she touched it or missed it?

"That was a lucky shot!" the tall boy exclaimed, going a little red.

"It wasn't luck," Nadia retorted.

"Come on, Jordan," one of the other boys said. Jordan glanced awkwardly at Nadia, then hurried to catch up with his friends.

"Great kick," Jack said, when they'd gone.

"Thanks," Nadia replied. "I'm going to be a professional footballer one day."

Jack grabbed his bag and headed towards a long, narrow red canal boat. "I live here," he said.

"You live on a boat?" Nadia said. "Cool!"

"Thanks," Jack replied.

"I live in the flats over there," Nadia said, pointing to a block of flats on the other side of the canal. "Better go. See you tomorrow at school!"

Chapter 2
The megaphone

On Saturday, Jack and his mum had breakfast in the boat's tiny kitchen.

"Can I borrow your tablet?" Jack asked, when he had finished.

"Of course," his mum said, with a smile.

"Thanks!" Jack climbed the steps to the rear deck and played on his favourite game.

After a few minutes, a woman strolled past. She dropped a sweet wrapper on the ground.

Jack stood up. "Please …" he began quietly, "can you pick your wrapper up and put it in the bin?"

"Pardon?" the woman said.

Jack repeated himself.

"There aren't any bins," the woman objected.

That was true. Well, there was one, but it was back along the canal path. Jack sat back down, and the woman walked away without picking up the sweet wrapper.

Jack wished he was confident, like Nadia. His voice felt so quiet at times; it was like it didn't <u>exist</u>. Then he had an idea. Mum's megaphone! He ran inside and fetched it. Jack's mum was a sports coach. She used the megaphone to shout instructions to the rowers as they went up and down the river. Jack switched the megaphone on. Perhaps this would help him to be bold, like Nadia had been yesterday.

Why did Jack feel like his voice didn't <u>exist</u>?

A few more people came past. Nervously, Jack got the megaphone ready, but they didn't drop any litter. Then he saw Nadia coming along the path. She was wearing her football kit and was carrying a ball under her arm.

"Hi," she called, as she came closer.

"Hello," Jack replied. He felt a little awkward. Should he invite her aboard?

The door to the cabin opened and his mum came out. Seeing Nadia in her football kit, she said, "Is this the football whizz you told me about, Jack?"

Nadia beamed, and Jack went a bit red. "Yes," he said, nodding.

"Hi, Nadia." His mum smiled. "Come aboard!"

"Thanks!" Nadia said, and Jack's mum helped her step across on to the boat.

"What are you doing with the megaphone?"
Jack's mum asked him. When he explained, she and
Nadia laughed.

"What's so funny?" Jack scowled. At that moment,
a passer-by tossed an empty drink can into the grass.

"Go on," Nadia whispered, and Jack's mum gave
him a nod. He raised the megaphone to his mouth
and took a breath.

"Please pick your rubbish up," Jack said. The megaphone made him sound like a giant robot.

The man looked up at him, startled. He pointed to himself and mouthed, "Me?"

"Yes, you," Jack boomed. "Please don't drop litter."

The man looked embarrassed. "Sorry," he said, and picked up the can. He smiled awkwardly and quickly walked away.

"Thank you!" Jack bellowed.

An elderly man called Mr Singh lived on a boat nearby. He was on his deck, watering his flowers, and had heard the whole thing. "Well said, Jack," he called.

"That was amazing!" Nadia grinned.

"Sometimes, we just need to ask politely and people will do the right thing," said Mr Singh.

Jack's mum beamed proudly, and Jack felt his face grow warm.

"I've got to go," Nadia said, picking up her ball. "I'm going to try out for the local football club."

"Good luck," Jack said. "I don't think you'll need it though," he added, as he remembered her kicking the tin can into the bin.

"Stop by any time you like, Nadia," Jack's mum said, smiling warmly.

"Thanks, I will," Nadia replied.

Just then, a duck landed on the roof of their boat.
Jack saw the curly tail feathers.

"That's the one you rescued, isn't it?" Mum said.

"I think so," Jack agreed.

"You'll have to think of a name for him if he's
going to be hanging around," said Mum.

"I'll call him …" he paused to think.

"Call him Bill!" came Mr Singh's voice, followed by
a wheezy laugh.

Jack laughed, too. "Bill … because of his …"

"Beak, yes!" Mr Singh chuckled.

"Very good, Mr Singh," Jack's mum said.

"All right," said Jack. "Hello, Bill. Welcome aboard."

Bill quacked, as if in reply.

Chapter 3
News spreads

Jack grew more confident at using the megaphone that weekend. Some passers-by told him they admired what he was doing. So did the people on the other boats. Nadia joined him for a while on Sunday, and they took it in turns with the megaphone.

On Monday morning at school, Mr Simmonds called the register. When he got to Jack, he said, "My sister lives on a boat near you, Jack."

Jack was flustered. "Really?" he said.

"Yes. She tells me you've been disturbing the peace with your megaphone."

Jack blushed, and Nadia looked up from her book.

"She thinks you're doing a wonderful job," Mr Simmonds finished.

Jack let out a long breath, and Nadia grinned.

"Perhaps you could tell the class about it,"
Mr Simmonds said.

Jack looked round at the class. His mouth dried
up, and the words would not come out.

Nadia glanced at him and then at Mr Simmonds.
"Can I tell them?" she asked.

To Jack's relief, Mr Simmonds nodded.

That evening, Jack, his mum and Nadia were sitting on the deck of the boat sipping squash. A tall man with a camera came along the canal path. He dropped a piece of paper, and immediately Jack's voice boomed through the megaphone, "Please take your litter home."

The man grinned and picked up the paper. "Ah," he said. "The famous Jack, I presume?"

"Famous?" Jack bellowed, and then he put down the megaphone. "Famous?" he repeated, in his normal voice.

"Yes, you've become quite a local celebrity. I'm from the newspaper," the man said. "Are you available for an interview?"

The man's name was Tariq, and he was a reporter. Jack's mum made Tariq a cup of tea, and he got out his pen and notebook.

Tariq asked Jack if he was available for an interview. Can you think of another way of saying this?

There was a flurry of wings behind them, and Bill landed on the boat.

"Hello there," Jack said, seeing the duck.

"It was because of Bill that Jack started all this," Nadia explained, and she told Tariq the story.

"Well," Tariq smiled, "I think people will love reading about all three of you."

Chapter 4
The competition

The following Saturday, Jack, his mum and Nadia walked to the newsagents together. They bought a newspaper and opened it excitedly. There was Tariq's article, complete with a photo of Jack, Nadia and Bill. The headline read: LOCAL TRIO CLEANS UP!

LOCAL TRIO CLEANS UP!

On Monday, Jack took the newspaper to school and Nadia read it out to the class.

"You should be very proud of yourselves," Mr Simmonds told Jack and Nadia. "Have you seen this?" he asked, turning the page of the newspaper. "I think it might interest you."

"The town council is running a competition," Jack read to Nadia, as Mr Simmonds returned to his desk. "Children have to send in their ideas for improving the local environment, and the council will put the winning idea into action."

"We should enter it," Nadia said.

Jack nodded. "It would be great to have some more bins along the canal path and some 'No littering' signs." He continued reading. "Entrants will be asked to present their <u>vision</u> in writing, using pictures, maps and diagrams." The next bit made him freeze. "They will also be asked to give a short speech."

What do you think Jack and Nadia's <u>vision</u> for the canal path might be?

"You'll have to do the speaking, Nadia," Jack said.

"OK. When is it?" Nadia asked, and Jack pointed at the date.

"Oh," Nadia said. "There's an important football match that day. There will be talent scouts from the county team there. Can you do it?"

"Me?" Jack gasped. "I hate talking in public!"

"You two can continue to hatch your plans later," interrupted Mr Simmonds. "It's time for maths."

At break, Nadia followed Jack outside. "Don't worry. I can take on the <u>role</u> of speaker and do the speech," she said.

"Are you sure?" Jack replied. "What about your match?"

Nadia shrugged. "There will be other matches," she said.

"Thanks." Jack wondered why he still felt glum.

How would Nadia be suited to the <u>role</u> of speaker? What else has she done in the story to show us she would be good at this <u>role</u>?

Jack walked home from school by himself as Nadia was at football practice. Coming the other way, he saw some of the teenagers he and Nadia had met on the canal path. The tall boy, Jordan, was drinking water from a plastic bottle. As they got closer to Jack, Jordan swigged the last of his water. Jack stared at the empty bottle in the boy's hand.

"Was that you I saw in the paper?" Jordan asked. When Jack nodded, Jordan said, "It's pretty cool, what you've been doing." Then he grinned at Jack and tucked his empty bottle into his bag.

"Maybe," Jack thought, "people are starting to take notice."

Chapter 5
The real winner

Every night that week, Nadia came to visit Jack on his boat. They drew a map of the canal and marked where the bins could go. They designed signs telling people not to drop litter. They interviewed Mr Singh and some of the other canal residents about the littering. Then they put it all together in a folder and dropped it off at the council offices after school on Friday.

As they walked home, Jack stared at the ground and didn't speak. For some reason, he couldn't look at Nadia. He wanted to feel excited about their project, but he couldn't. The speeches were due to take place on Saturday, but he didn't have to worry about theirs because Nadia was going to do it. So why did he feel so bad?

Jack knew what he had to do.

As they arrived at the boat, he said, "Nadia, I'll do the speech."

Nadia blinked. "Are you sure?"

"Honestly, I want to do it," he said, nodding. "I'm sorry I was going to let you miss the match. I feel awful. You're amazing at football. You have to play."

Nadia grinned, and suddenly, Jack felt a lot better.

 Which of these words is the opposite of 'honest': unhonest or dishonest? Do you think it is a good thing that Jack spoke honestly about his feelings?

Jack practised his speech over and over again, and his mum told him how wonderful it was. He was getting better and better at it, but he couldn't help imagining what the judges would be like. In his mind, they were terrifying giants that were laughing at him.

On Saturday, Jack and his mum took the bus into town.

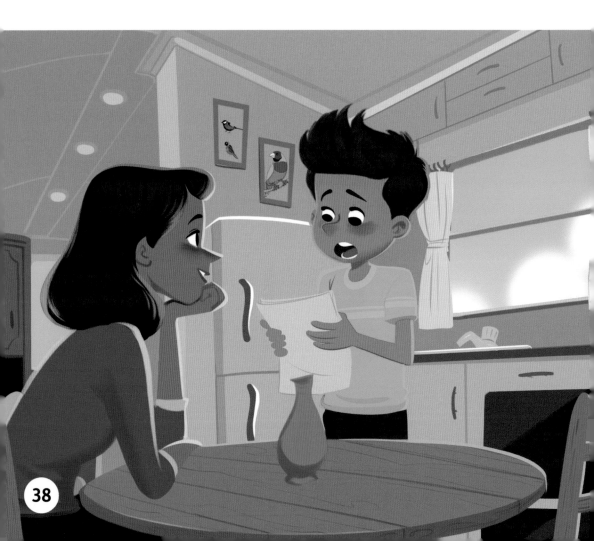

They arrived at the council offices. There were four judges sitting behind a long table in a big room. They didn't look terrifying at all. In fact, they were very friendly. There were chairs for all the parents and the other children taking part. Jack waited with his mum while the first few speeches were given. The children all sounded confident, and their ideas were great.

Then Jack's name was called. His mum gave him a smile.

Jack made his way slowly to the front. Behind him, there came a sudden burst of cheering. He turned and saw his mum was sitting with Mr Singh and other people from the canal boats. Jack hadn't known they were there! He smiled. As he walked towards the judges, he passed Tariq who waved his notebook and grinned at Jack.

Jack took a deep breath. He opened his mouth and was surprised to find that the words came out easily. As he went on, the judges nodded and made notes. When he had finished, the crowd clapped and his mum cheered. He breathed a sigh of relief.

There was a break while the judges made their decision. Jack's mum came over to see him with the other people from the boats.

"You were fantastic!" Mr Singh said.

Jack couldn't stop smiling.

Finally, it was time to sit back down to find out the results ...

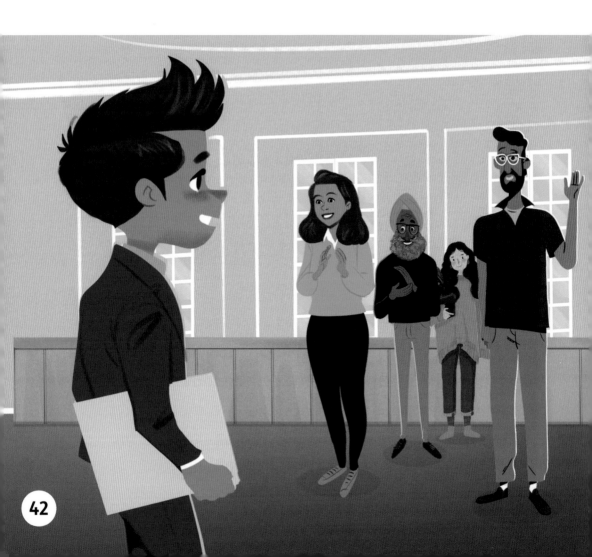

Jack didn't win. He came second, but he didn't mind. The winning idea was to have speed bumps outside the school. "The speed bumps could save children's lives," thought Jack. "That idea deserved to win."

As a treat, Jack's mum took him to a cafe for a piece of cake. It was late afternoon when they got back to the canal. A big surprise was waiting.

Mr Singh and their other friends were all gathered around their boat, cheering and applauding. They had tied a banner to the bridge. It read: *Jack, our hero!* Along the fence, they had fixed home-made signs which read: *Please use our litter bins.* On a nearby bin, someone had stencilled a duck holding a megaphone.

"My idea," Mr Singh said, grinning proudly and looking at the duck stencils.

"Also, we now have <u>multiple</u> bins," Jack's mum pointed out.

Jack saw bins all along the path, also stencilled with the duck and megaphone.

"Does this mean we won, then?" came Nadia's voice from behind him. Jack turned and saw her coming down the steps, muddy and tired.

Why do you think it's important to have <u>multiple</u> bins along the canal path, rather than just one?

"No," Jack said. "But we came second."

"Wow!" Nadia cried. "That's brilliant. Look at all the signs and bins! We didn't need to win the competition after all."

"How did you get on?" Jack asked.

"They picked me for the team!" Nadia replied, and punched the air.

Everyone clapped and cheered for her.

Bill was swimming nearby, and he gave a little
quack, as if he knew exactly what had happened.
Jack and Nadia laughed and waved at him.

In the days that followed, the bins filled with litter,
and no one dropped anything on the path. Jack put
the megaphone away. He no longer needed it.

Read and discuss

Read and talk about the following questions.

Page 2: Jack lives near the city's <u>central</u> park. What does this tell us about where in the city Jack lives – near the middle or on the edge?

Page 8: What happened when Nadia's foot made <u>contact</u> with the can?

Page 13: Can you think of something that does not really <u>exist</u>?

Page 26: Which days after school are you <u>available</u> to play with your friends?

Page 30: What would your <u>vision</u> be to improve where you live?

Page 32: Was Jack suited to the <u>role</u> of speaker in the end? Why?/Why not?

Page 37: Do you think it is important to always be <u>honest</u>? Why?/Why not?

Page 45: Can you think of a word or phrase that means the same thing as '<u>multiple</u>'?